WINIFRED HOLTBY
SCHOOL LRC

C000176106

FANTASTIC

ANNUAL 2006

WHAT'S INSIDE

5 STRIP ADVENTURE:
The Skrulls From Outer Space!
The Fantastic Four protect the planet from
an alien invasion in this exciting story!

17 FANTASTI-FILE#1: Mister Fantastic

18 MISSION OF DOOM:
Help the F4 defeat Doctor Doom by
solving the puzzles in this mission!

20 FANTASTI-FILE#2:
The Invisible Woman

**21 STRIP ADVENTURE: The Skrulls
From Outer Space!** (Part 2)

31 STRIP QUIZ:
See how much of the story you
remember by taking this quiz!

**32 ENEMIES OF THE FANTASTIC
FOUR:**
Check out this roundup of
10 vicious villains!

34 COLOUR ZONE:
Grab your pens and add some colour
to this action scene!

36 FANTASTI-FILE#3: The Human Torch

37 STRIP ADVENTURE:
Prisoners Of Doom!
The dastardly Doctor Doom sends
the F4 on a dangerous mission

47 F4 IDENTITY CRISIS:
Take this quiz to discover your
F4 match

48 FANTASTI-FILE#4: The Thing

49 STRIP ADVENTURE:
Prisoners Of Doom! (Part 2)

61 STRIP QUIZ:
See how much of the story you
remember by taking this quiz!

62 ANSWERS PAGE

£6.99

FANTASTIC 4 EARTH'S FIRST FAMILY OF SUPER HEROES!

▶ Reed Richards – a brilliant scientist. Benjamin Grimm –
▶ his best friend. Sue Storm – the woman he loves.
And Johnny Storm – her fiery kid brother. Together,
they rocketed into space in an experimental spaceship,
the first humans to attempt interstellar travel.

But a freak encounter with cosmic rays changed their
lives forever, granting each of them unique powers.
They became Mister Fantastic, the Invisible Woman,
the Thing, and the Human Torch!

From that day forward they began new lives. Financed by Reed's
inventions, they set up headquarters in the Baxter Building in
New York City. But they are not Super Heroes in the traditional
sense. They don't fight crime or patrol the streets of the city...

They are **astronauts**, **explorers**, and **trailblazers**! They are the greatest squad of
superhuman adventurers ever assembled, continuing to push the bounds of human exploration.

And most importantly -- whatever
dangers they face, **they face as a family!**

WINIFRED HOLTBY LRC
DATE. 15·12·05
PRICE. 6.99
CLASS. 791

IRRADIATED BY COSMIC RAYS, THEY JOINED TOGETHER TO FIGHT EVIL. **MISTER FANTASTIC**, THE **INVISIBLE WOMAN**, THE **HUMAN TORCH** AND THE **THING**. TOGETHER THEY CALL THEMSELVES THE **FANTASTIC FOUR** *IN*

"--there will be no one to stop us from *invading Earth!*"

THE FANTASTIC FOUR MEET THE SKRULLS FROM OUTER SPACE!

Stan Lee & Jack Kirby	Sean McKeever	Gurihuri	SotoColor's J. Roberts, J. Keith & Soto	Dave Sharpe
PLOT	WRITER	ARTIST	COLORS	LETTERER
MacKenzie Cadenhead	C.B. Cebulski	Ralph Macchio	Joe Quesada	Dan Buckley
ASSISTANT EDITOR	EDITOR	CONSULTING EDITOR	EDITOR-IN-CHIEF	PUBLISHER

15

CONTINUED ON PAGE 21

FANTASTI-FILES #1

MR. FANTASTIC

One of the most intelligent people on Earth, and possessing fantastic stretching abilities, Reed Richards is leader of the fabulous FANTASTIC FOUR!

PERSONAL DATA

Real Name: Reed Richards
Height: 6'1"
Weight: 180 lbs.
Eye Colour: Brown
Hair Colour: Brown, with greying temples
Powers: Can stretch or compress his body into any shape he can imagine
Abilities: Scientific genius
Quote: "...core destabilisation in point one nanoseconds...."

The brains of the team, Reed Richards uses his fantastic genius to explore the mysteries of outer space. Since receiving his amazing stretching powers, he has invented countless cool devices to help mankind. He's always buried in his work, so sometimes he can forget his teammates. But Sue is always on hand to remind him to take a break from time to time.

REED'S INVENTIONS:

Unstable Molecules
Pocket Rocket
Fantasticar
X-Ray Camera
Invisibility Ray
Fireproof Plastic
Beta-Ray Gun

FILM REEL

In the movie, Reed is played by the actor **Ioan Gruffudd**

FANTASTIC POWERS

It's cool being stretchy! Reed can bend his body into all sorts of useful shapes, like parachutes and bridges. He can make himself as thin as a sheet of paper - useful for sneaking through doorways. Plus he can stretch his body into a shield to protect his teammates - and bullets and missiles just bounce right off him!

FANTASTI-FACT: Ben Grimm has given Reed the nickname "Stretch"

17

MISSION OF DOOM!

▶ Help the Fantastic Four defeat
▶ the diabolical Doctor Doom
by completing all the puzzles
in this comic story! ▶▶▶▶▶

▶▶ A NORMAL DAY IN THE *BAXTER BUILDING*, HEADQUARTERS OF EARTH'S MOST FAMOUS SUPER HEROES, THE *FANTASTIC FOUR!*

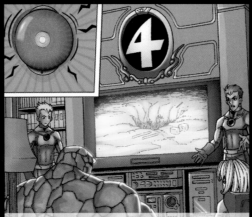

SUDDENLY AN *ALARM* SOUNDS! *DOCTOR DOOM* HAS STOLEN AN ANCIENT AMULET OF GREAT POWER FROM THE CITY MUSEUM!

WE BETTER GET TO THE MUSEUM AND STOP DOOM, *DOUBLE-TIME!*

WITH NO TIME TO WASTE, THE TEAM GEAR UP FOR THEIR MISSION!

TIME TRIAL

Work out which is the quickest route to the Museum by adding or subtracting the time delays on each journey. Hurry, before Doom escapes!

ROUTE 1
SMOKESCREEN +5
-2 TURBO BOOST
BREAKDOWN +3
+6 WRONG TURN

TOTAL :00 MINS

ROUTE 2
ASK DIRECTIONS +4
+5 ONE WAY STREET
SHORT CUT -6
BAD WEATHER +4

TOTAL :00 MINS

ROUTE 3
+5 STOPPED BY THE COPS
DETOUR +6
-4 SPEED BURST
STOP SIGN +5

TOTAL :00 MINS

DESTINATION
NEW YORK CITY MUSEUM

DIMENSION DASH

▶▶▶▶ Help Reed Richards open up a portal to Latveria! You've got to press the correct button on the teleport keypad – get it wrong and you could end up anywhere!

BAD LUCK, FANTASTI-FOOLS! YOU'RE NO MATCH FOR *DOCTOR DOOM!*

IT'S TOO LATE! DOOM HAS TELEPORTED BACK TO *LATVERIA*, THE SMALL COUNTRY IN EUROPE WHERE HE RULES SUPREME. BUT HE'S LEFT HIS PORTAL DEVICE BEHIND. COULD THE FANTASTIC FOUR USE IT TO GIVE CHASE?

The button has a skull symbol on it.

The button does NOT have the colour red on it.

The button does NOT have a hand symbol on it.

The button has a serpent symbol on it.

TELEPORTAL

PRESS CORRECT KEY FOR ENTRY

BREAK-IN!

START

Find a safe route into Doom Castle, avoiding any dead-ends along the way!

THE FANTASTIC FOUR ARE TELEPORTED INSTANTLY TO THE GROUNDS OF **DOOM'S CASTLE** IN LATVERIA. BUT TO GET TO HIM, THEY FIRST HAVE TO GET PAST HIS **CASTLE DEFENCES!**

Doom Castle

OUR HEROES HAVE MADE IT SAFELY INTO THE CASTLE, BUT NOW THEY HAVE A MUCH BIGGER PROBLEM... **DOOMBOTS!**

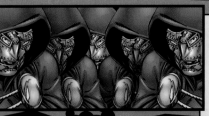

DOOM HAS HIDDEN HIMSELF AMONGST A WHOLE ARMY POWERFUL WARRIOR ROBOTS THAT LOOK ALMOST IDENTICAL TO HIM! HOW CAN THE F4 FIND HIM?

Legions of Doom

Can you help the Fantastic Four locate the dreaded Doctor? Find the Doom which is a perfect match to the image on the data file!

A

B

C

D

SUCCESS! THE FANTASTIC FOUR HAVE DEFEATED THE DOOMBOTS, AND THE REAL DOCTOR DOOM HAS BEEN **CAPTURED!**

AND THE PRECIOUS AMULET HAS BEEN RECOVERED SAFELY, AND TAKEN BACK TO THE MUSEUM WHERE IT BELONGS!

MISSION ACCOMPLISHED!

INVISIBLE WOMAN

With the ability to create forcefields and turn invisible, Sue is the heart and soul of the Fantastic Four!

PERSONAL DATA

Real Name: Sue Richards
Height: 5'6"
Weight: 120 lbs.
Eye Colour: Blue
Hair Colour: Blonde
Powers: Can turn herself and other objects invisible – can project invisible forcefields
Quote: "Quit arguing you two!"

Always on hand to step in when Johnny and Ben start bickering, Sue is the mother of the team, and the glue that holds the F4 together. But she's no pushover in battle - villains who underestimate her power usually pay the price, for there's nothing she wouldn't do to protect the lives of those she loves!

FANTASTI-FACT:

Susan Richards designed the Fantastic Four's costumes.

FILM REEL

In the movie, Sue is played by the actress **Jessica Alba**

FANTASTIC POWERS

Not only can Sue turn herself invisible for long periods, she can turn other people and objects invisible too. In addition, she can create forcefields to protect herself and the rest of the team from attacks. Plus, by projecting energy beneath her, she can travel through the air.

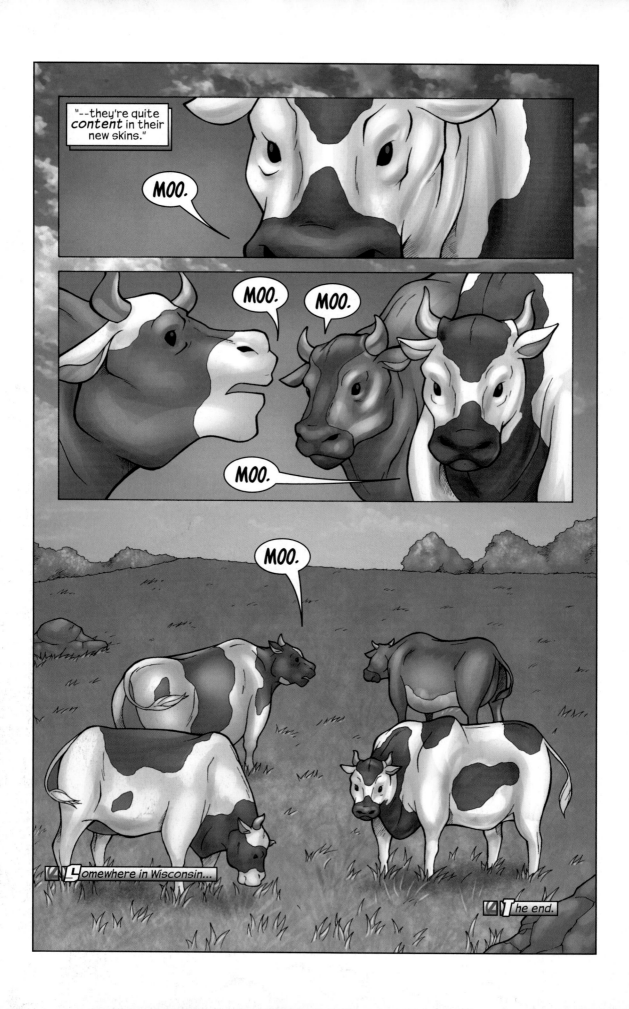

F4 BRAIN SQUEEZE!

The Skrulls have turned tail and fled, and it's all thanks to the heroic Fantastic Four. But how closely were **YOU** paying attention!?

See how many questions you can answer, **WITHOUT LOOKING BACK AT THE STORY!**

ANSWERS ON PAGE 62!

▶▶1 Take a look at these panels taken from the story. We've blanked out one character in each – can you identify who it is?

later... So, we've captured our doppelgangers, but there's still an **army** waiting to invade Earth.

How do we stop them, Reed?

Reed, you're not actually *considering* their offer, are you?

2 ▶▶ Which of these creatures did the Skrulls *NOT* change into in the story?

A: Doves
B: Cows
C: Leopards
D: Monsters

3 ▶▶ We've blanked out what Ben is saying in this picture taken from the strip. Look at the speech balloons and identify the correct one!

FANTASTIC PUBLIC ENE

A AWW NUTS! THE YANKEE'S LOST AGAIN!

B JUST WHAT IN THE WORLD IS GOIN' ON HERE??

C WOW! THERE'S A SALE AT MACY'S!

D NEVER NUTHIN' GOOD TA READ THESE DAYS!

4 ◢ Take a look at this picture of the triumphant Fantastic Four, and try to spot 5 things that shouldn't be there!

HELLO MUM!

5 ◢ What was the Skrull spaceship disguised as in the story?

A: Water tower B: Skyscraper C: City bus D: Hot Dog stand

ONE DAY, THE *SKRULLS* WILL RULE THE *UNIVERSE!*

ENEMIES OF THE F4!

The universe and beyond is often not a very safe place. Here are some of the bad guys the Fantastic Four will have to watch out for!

GALACTUS

One of the most powerful beings in existence, Galactus is a giant humanoid of god-like strength and intelligence. He travels the cosmos aboard his advanced starship, seeking out suitable planets on which to feed to sustain his life force.

THREAT LEVEL: 10 out of 10

BLASTAAR

Former King of the planet Baluur, the superhumanly powerful Blastaar is a constant threat to Earth. Able to shoot concussive force beams from his fingertips, the evil alien can also fly at great speed, and resist almost all forms of damage, including heat, cold and large calibre bullets.

THREAT LEVEL: 7 out of 10

MOLECULE MAN

A nuclear accident gave Molecule Man the ability to expand his molecular structure so that solid objects pass right through him.
Also, he can condense his molecules, making his body as tough as steel. But the biggest danger is that he can dissolve his foes by 'demagnetizing' their molecules!

THREAT LEVEL: 5 out of 10

DOCTOR DOOM

A brilliant but arrogant scientist, Victor Von Doom was disfigured when one of his early experiments went horribly wrong. Now, with his scarred face masked by a metal faceplate, Dr. Doom rules the small European country of Latveria with an iron fist. His ultimate aim is world domination...and the destruction of the fabled Fantastic Four!

THREAT LEVEL: 9 out of 10

MOLE MAN

After being shunned because of his hideous appearance, Mole Man conquered the people of the underground realm of Subterranea and became their king. Now, with his moloid monster hordes, he seeks revenge on the surface dwellers for his suffering!

THREAT LEVEL: 7 out of 10

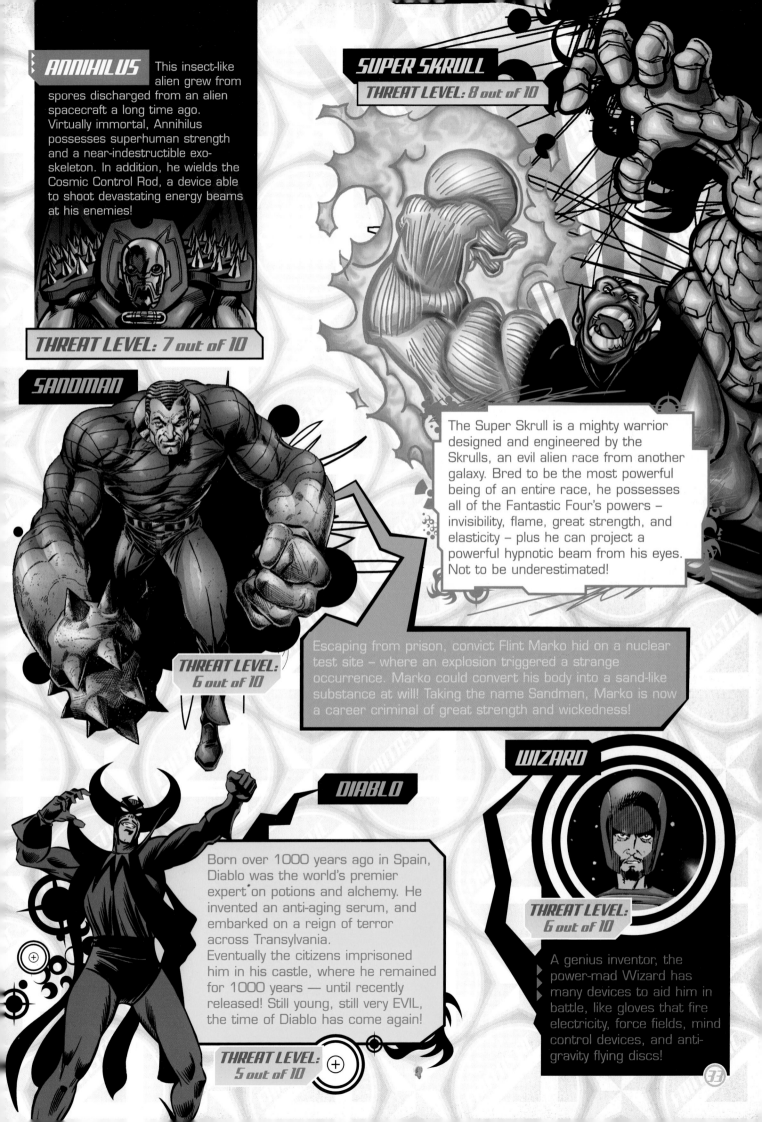

ANNIHILUS This insect-like alien grew from spores discharged from an alien spacecraft a long time ago. Virtually immortal, Annihilus possesses superhuman strength and a near-indestructible exo-skeleton. In addition, he wields the Cosmic Control Rod, a device able to shoot devastating energy beams at his enemies!

THREAT LEVEL: 7 out of 10

SUPER SKRULL

THREAT LEVEL: 8 out of 10

The Super Skrull is a mighty warrior designed and engineered by the Skrulls, an evil alien race from another galaxy. Bred to be the most powerful being of an entire race, he possesses all of the Fantastic Four's powers – invisibility, flame, great strength, and elasticity – plus he can project a powerful hypnotic beam from his eyes. Not to be underestimated!

SANDMAN

THREAT LEVEL: 6 out of 10

Escaping from prison, convict Flint Marko hid on a nuclear test site – where an explosion triggered a strange occurrence. Marko could convert his body into a sand-like substance at will! Taking the name Sandman, Marko is now a career criminal of great strength and wickedness!

WIZARD

DIABLO

Born over 1000 years ago in Spain, Diablo was the world's premier expert on potions and alchemy. He invented an anti-aging serum, and embarked on a reign of terror across Transylvania.
Eventually the citizens imprisoned him in his castle, where he remained for 1000 years — until recently released! Still young, still very EVIL, the time of Diablo has come again!

THREAT LEVEL: 5 out of 10

THREAT LEVEL: 6 out of 10

A genius inventor, the power-mad Wizard has many devices to aid him in battle, like gloves that fire electricity, force fields, mind control devices, and anti-gravity flying discs!

COLOUR ZONE

The F4 are under attack from a multitude of malicious maniacs!
Load up your pens and crayons and bring this explosive action scene to life!

There are 10 **Data Cubes** and 10 **Stun Grenades** hidden in this picture.
Can you find them all?

74

HUMAN TORCH

With amazing flame powers and a fiery personality to match, the Human Torch is the daredevil of the Fantastic Four!

PERSONAL DATA

Real Name: Johnny Storm
Height: 5'10"
Weight: 170 lbs.
Eye Colour: Blue
Hair Colour: Blond
Powers: Can sheathe his body in fire – shoot fire – fly
Abilities: Expert racing car driver
Quote: "FLAME ON!"

Johnny Storm is the hothead of the Fantastic Four, and the baby of the bunch. A brave and loyal teammate, sometimes the Torch rushes into battle without considering the consequences. And he has a quite a talent for tormenting the Thing, but Sue and Reed are always on hand to keep him in check!

FANTASTIC POWERS

The Torch can shoot fireballs of all shapes and sizes, but his most powerful attack is the NOVA FLAME. This white-hot flame can be as hot as 1 million degrees, and Johnny claims it can destroy a small moon! In addition, the Torch can fly at speeds of up to 140 mph, and can form his flame trails into letters and shapes in the sky.

FILM REEL

In the movie, Johnny is played by the actor **Chris Evans**

FANTASTI-FACT:

How does Johnny never burn his costume when he flames on? Because it's made from unstable molecules, one of Reed's inventions, so it never gets damaged!

DAILY BU...

FANTASTIC FOUR SAVES CITY FROM MARINE MENACE

IRRADIATED BY COSMIC RAYS, THEY JOINED TOGETHER TO FIGHT EVIL. **MISTER FANTASTIC,** THE **INVISIBLE WOMAN,** THE **HUMAN TORCH** AND THE **THING.** TOGETHER THEY CALL THEMSELVES THE **FANTASTIC FOUR** in

The Fantastic Four! Hah!

Little do they realize that they are but pawns in my master plan!

The time has finally come to make my presence known--

--for only I have the power to defeat them once and for all!

Soon, Reed Richards, you and your accursed allies will be...

PRISONERS OF DOCTOR DOOM

Stan Lee & Jack Kirby
PLOT

Marc Sumerak
WRITER

Udon's Dax Gordine w/ M3TH
ARTISTS

Gotham
COLORS

Dave Sharpe
LETTERER

MacKenzie Cadenhead & John Barber
ASSISTANT EDITORS

C.B. Cebulski
EDITOR

Ralph Macchio
CONSULTING EDITOR

Joe Quesada
EDITOR-IN-CHIEF

Dan Buckley
PUBLISHER

Return with me to aid my cause--or *fall* as the *first casualties* in *Doom's* supreme reign!

Signal your surrender...or face the *wrath of Doom!*

You heard Doom. Send up the signal, Johnny.

But, Reed--I know we can take this guy!

THE SIGNAL, JOHNNY!

A *wise* choice, Richards.

As a man of my word, I spare your lives and welcome you into the service of Doom.

Knowing you are a man of your word as well, I trust that you will not attempt to *double-cross* me.

Keep your cohorts in line and you all still stand a chance at survival.

"Keep us in line"?!? Can you *believe* this bum?

Unfortunately, we have *no choice,* Ben.

Even years ago, Doom was a *dangerous* man. If he's somehow managed to *increase* his abilities...

But what does any of this have to do with us?

The Doom I know would *never* have sought us out unless he depended on our abilities to get what he needs. He must be after something *important.*

Once we figure out what his *plan* is, all we need to do is wait for the *right opportunity...*

And *then* it's clobberin' time?

Then and *only* then.

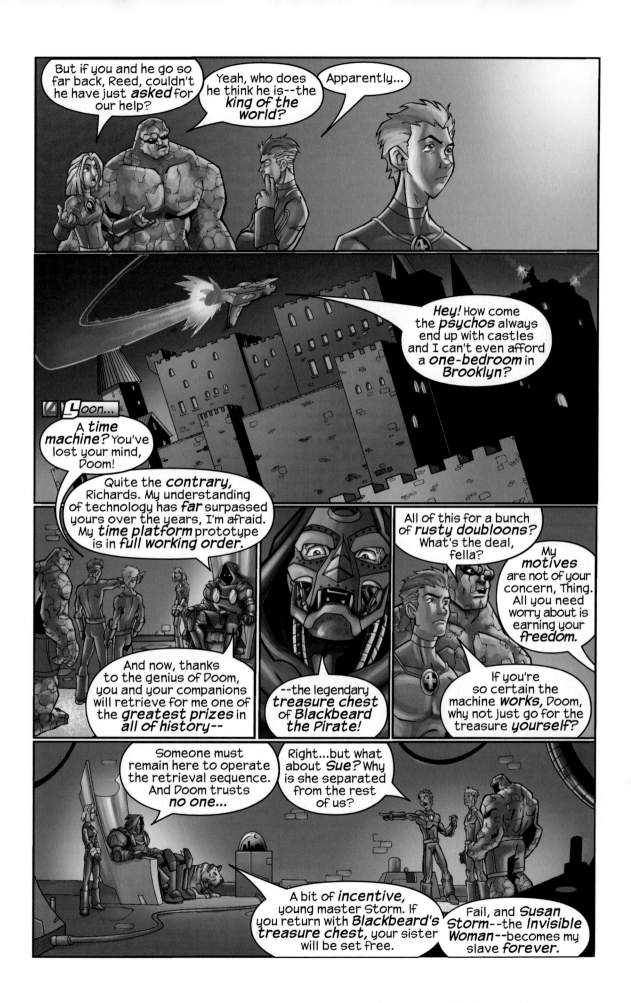

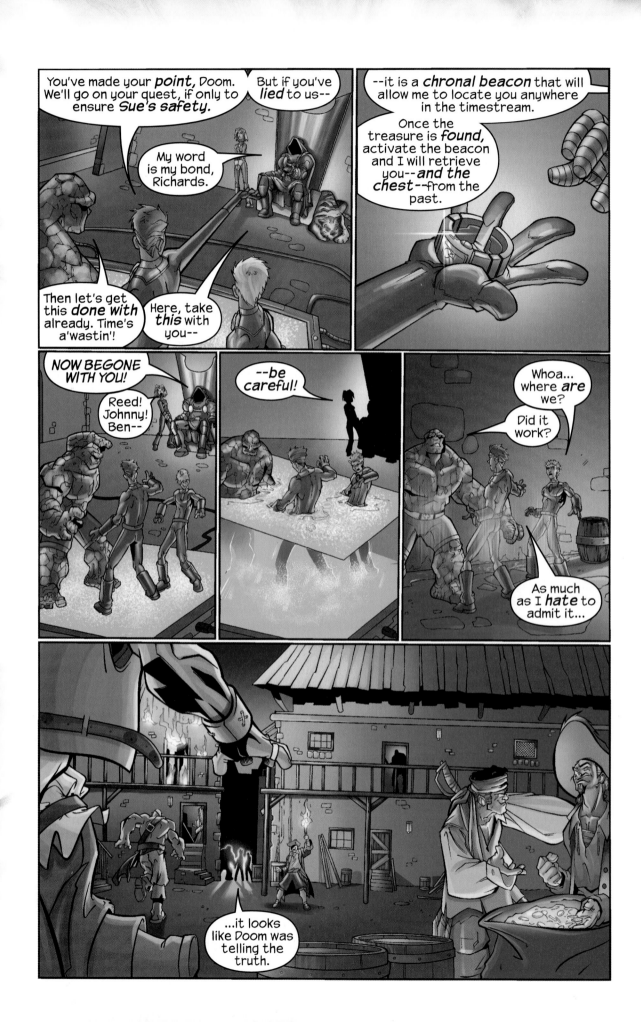

CONTINUED ON PAGE 49

46

IDENTITY CRISIS!

Take this quiz to find out which F4 member you most resemble.
Answer the questions and let the arrows guide you to your perfect match!

You're watching TV when a special news bulletin reports that aliens are attacking your town. Do you...

Jump on your skateboard and head into town to investigate

Check the internet for more info on the invaders

Make yourself a cheese sandwich

You suddenly find yourself beamed aboard one of the alien spacecrafts. Do you...

Aliens barge into your bedroom! What do you do?

Dive head-first through a nearby trap door

Give yourself up

Hide, then follow the aliens back to their spaceship

Try and communicate with them

You end up inside a prison cell aboard their spaceship. What's your escape plan?

You find yourself in the ship's control room. What's your next move?

Grab a space-suit and laser gun and leap out the ship's airlock, torching the ship on your way down

Clobber all the aliens, then trash the ship's flight computer, causing it to crash-land

Hide in the shadows and stun the guard when he brings you some food, then sneak off the ship to warn your friends

Pick the lock with a piece of wire, then upload a data virus into a wall-terminal to trash the ship's computer

HUMAN TORCH

You are courageous and daring, just like the Human Torch! You love to take risks and have a good time, but sometimes you should stop and think before diving in!

THE THING

Never one to back down from a fight, you prefer to let your fists do the talking, just like the Thing. You're loyal, honest and forthright, but maybe should try to control your temper once in a while!

INVISIBLE WOMAN

Like Sue, you are resourceful and determined, and there's nothing you wouldn't do to help your friends.
You prefer not to be the centre of attention, but if need be you can take the starring role!

MR. FANTASTIC

Like Mister Fantastic, you know that problems are often best solved with brainpower, not brawn. You always get absorbed in your work, so it's important to remember to lighten up from time to time!

FANTASTI-FILES #4

THE THING

≋④

A man-mountain of orange stone, the Thing uses his superhuman strength to protect his teammates and battle the bad guys!

PERSONAL DATA

Real Name: Benjamin Grimm
Height: 6'
Weight: 500 lbs.
Eye Colour: Blue
Hair Colour: Brown in human form, none as the Thing
Powers: Superhuman strength and endurance – tough, rock-like skin
Quote: "IT'S CLOBBERIN' TIME!"

Once a skilled fighter-pilot, Ben Grimm is now the Thing, a hideous creature of craggy, orange stone with superhuman strength and toughness.
The only one of team unable to change back to human form, Ben has nonetheless maintained his sense of humour and honour – because under that rocky exterior lies an ever-lovin' heart of gold!

FILM REEL

In the movie, Ben is played by the actor **Michael Chiklis** ▶

FANTASTI-FACT:

The Thing can hold his breath under water for almost 9 minutes.

FANTASTIC POWERS

The Thing's primary power is his massive strength. He can lift about 85 tons - that's the weight of 11 elephants! Plus his rocky skin is almost totally resistant to injury - he can take a bazooka shell in the chest with no damage. And don't let his size fool you - his reflexes are pretty sharp too!

CONTINUED FROM PAGE 46

Aw, crud... When ya put it that way...

Alright, Reed... activate Doom's time-thingy before I change my mind and have the both of ya *walk the plank!*

That's the spirit, Benny-boy!

With the *chronal beacon* activated, it should only be a matter of moments before Doom receives our signal--

--locks in on our location in *time* and *space*--

--and takes us safely back--

Ah! My emissaries have returned *triumphant,* as I knew you would!

--to the *present!*

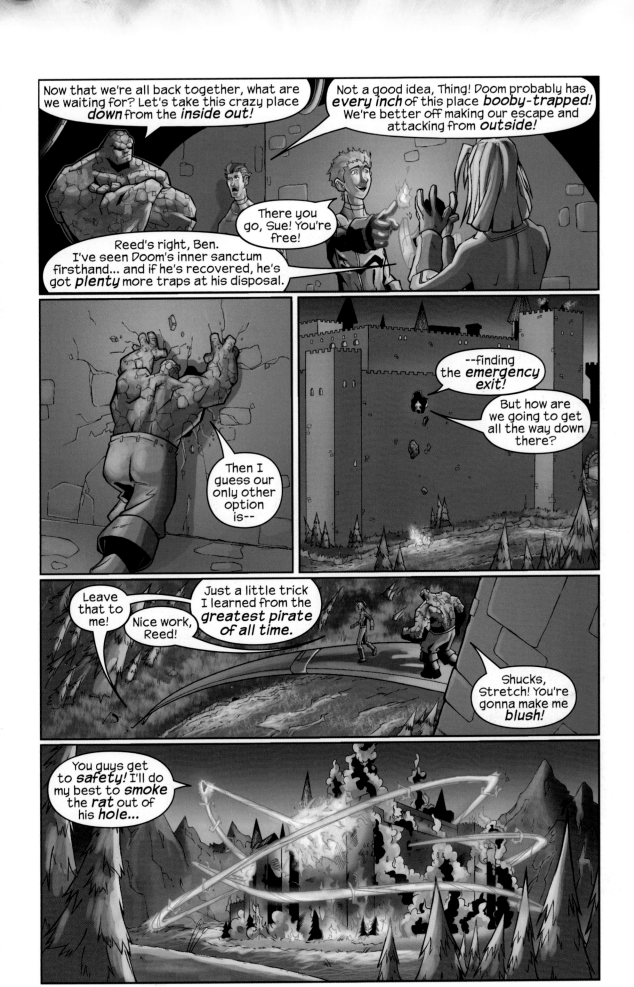

F4 BRAIN SQUEEZE! #2

With Doom defeated and his evil plans thwarted, the mighty Fantastic Four are once again triumphant. But let's see how much of their adventure YOU can remember!

See how many questions you can answer, WITHOUT LOOKING BACK AT THE STORY!

1 What DVD are the Fantastic Four watching at the start of the story?

A: X-Men
B: Hulk
C: Star Wars
D: Free Willy

2 How do the Fantastic Four signal their surrender to Doom?

A: A white flag
B: They put down weapons
C: Johnny creates a fire signal in the sky of the number 4

3 Look at this picture of the old world Tavern in the story, and try to spot 4 objects too modern to be there!

5 What does Reed Richards put in Blackbeard's chest after he has tipped out the treasure?

A: Rocks   **C:** Apples
B: Sand   **D:** Chains

4 When the Thing made himself captain, what name did he give to the pirate ship?

A: The Salty Dog
B: The Fanasti-boat
C: The Crusty Bucket
D: The Blue Barnacle

ANSWERS ON PAGE 62!

6 Finally, put these four panels in the order that they appear in the story!

ANSWERS!

HEY! ARE YOU CHEATING? ONLY LOOK AT THIS PAGE WHEN YOU THINK YOU'VE SOLVED ALL THE PUZZLES IN THIS ANNUAL!

18 MISSION OF DOOM!

TIME TRIAL

Route 1 = 12 minutes
Route 2 = 7 minutes
Route 3 = 12 minutes
Route 2 is the fastest route!

DIMENSION DASH

Button 9 opens the portal!

The safe route to the castle has been shown on the maze below in RED.

Legions of Doom

The real Doctor Doom is **C**

F4 BRAIN SQUEEZE! 31

Question 1
A: Mister Fantastic
B: The Human Torch
C: The Thing
D: The Invisible Woman

Question 2
C - Leopards

Question 3
B:

JUST WHAT IN THE WORLD IS GOIN' ON HERE??

The five objects that shouldn't be there have been circled on the scene in RED.

Question 5
A - Water Tower

COLOUR ZONE

34
The 10 data cubes have been circled in GREEN. The 10 stun grenades have been circled in RED.

HOPE Y'ALL ENJOYED THIS ANNUAL! NOW GET OUT OF HERE YA MOOKS!

F4 BRAIN SQUEEZE!

Question 1 = B - Hulk

Question 2
C - Johnny creates a fire signal in the sky

Question 4
C - The Crusty Bucket

Question 3
The four objects too modern to be in the picture have been marked in RED.

Question 5
D - Chains

Question 6
The pictures appear in this order in the story: B - D - A - C

61